NEW PIECES FOR VIOLA · BO

THE ASSOCIATED BOARD OF
THE ROYAL SCHOOLS OF MUSIC

Contents

IDYLL

TIMOTHY BAXTER

A.B. 1545

6

A.B.1545

LAMENT

SEBASTIAN FORBES

MELODY
(A Folk Song)

MICHAEL HEAD

ALLA GRECO

TIMOTHY BAXTER

EVENING MIST

(No. 6 of Cameos for Viola)

KENNETH JONES

18

A.B.1545

SONG OF DELIGHT

(No. 7 of Cameos for Viola)

KENNETH JONES

RONDO

SEBASTIAN FORBES

CAPRICCIO

SEBASTIAN FORBES

28

A.B.1545

OUTWARDLY SERENE

STEPHEN DODGSON

DIVERTIMENTO
(Variations)

MICHAEL HEAD

Doppio movimento

* omit if played by viola

Tempo Primo

ossia * can be played an octave higher to *

piano part can be played an octave higher to end of piece

Printed in England by Caligraving Limited, Thetford, Norfolk

A.B.1545

7:90